PEANUTS

Snoopy Takes Off!

By Charles M. Schulz

Adapted by Tina Gallo

Illustrated by Scott Jeralds

SIMON SPOTLIGHT

New York   London   Toronto   Sydney   New Delhi

This is Snoopy. He may look like a regular dog to you, but in fact, he is anything but ordinary!

Snoopy doesn't do anything the same way as an ordinary dog, starting with the way he sleeps *on* his doghouse, rather than inside.

Charlie Brown is Snoopy's owner, although a lot of the time it seems like it's the other way around.

What a beautiful day, Snoopy thinks. *It's a perfect day for me to jump in my plane, soar through the air, and fight the Red Baron!*

When Snoopy says he is going to "jump in his plane," he really means he's going to sit on top of his doghouse. He puts on his goggles, scarf, and helmet. "Here's the World War One Flying Ace flying across the sky in his Sopwith Camel airplane," Snoopy says. "Where are you, Red Baron? You can't hide from me!"

Suddenly Snoopy spots the Red Baron's plane! "Yes!" he cheers. He is finally going to capture the enemy!

"Full speed ahead!" Snoopy shouts. But as fast as Snoopy is, the Red Baron is faster. He gets away . . . again. "Noooo!" Snoopy shouts, waving his fist. "I'll get you, Red Baron! Next time you are mine!"

Snoopy takes off his helmet and sits down with a sigh. He turns around and sees Charlie Brown standing with his food dish. Charlie Brown is shaking his head.

"I wonder what it would be like to have a normal dog," Charlie Brown tells him.

Snoopy ignores him and concentrates on enjoying his food. Being a World War I Flying Ace works up an appetite!

Later that afternoon Snoopy is bored, so he decides to write the next Great American Novel. He pulls out his trusty old typewriter and begins to write.

It was a dark and stormy night.

Linus walks by and is curious. "May I see what you've written?" he asks.

Snoopy nods and hands Linus the page.

"Your new novel has a very exciting beginning," Linus says.

Snoopy smiles proudly.

Linus hands back the sheet of paper. "Well, good luck with the second sentence," he says.

Lucy is curious about Snoopy's book too. She has a suggestion for him. "'It was a dark and stormy night' is a terrible way to begin a story," she says. "You should begin your story with 'Once upon a time.' That's the way all good stories begin."

Snoopy thinks Lucy may be right, so he changes the beginning of his story. He types:

Once upon a time, it was a dark and stormy night.

Lucy looks at the new sheet of paper and groans.

"Can't you write about something nice?" she asks Snoopy.

Snoopy thinks this is a good idea. So he types. Then he stops typing, and to Lucy's surprise, he jumps off his doghouse . . .

Once upon a time, it was a dark and stormy night. Suddenly, a kiss rang out!

and he gives Lucy a big kiss!

"Aaagh, I've been kissed by a dog! I've got dog germs!" Lucy cries, and runs away.

That wasn't nearly as romantic as I thought it would be, Snoopy thinks.

Snoopy decides it's time for a dance break! There's nothing Snoopy loves more than dancing!

He dances with Charlie Brown!

He dances with Lucy!

He dances with Linus!

He even dances on top of Schroeder's piano! (Schroeder doesn't like this very much.)

After all that dancing, it's time for a snack. Snoopy invites his best friend, Woodstock, to come over for some homemade cookies and milk. Even though Snoopy enjoys the dog food Charlie Brown brings him, he is also a fabulous cook, and loves whipping up surprises for his friends.

Woodstock loves hanging out with Snoopy and tells him all about his day. Fortunately for Woodstock, Snoopy is fluent in bird and understands every word he says.

Woodstock wants to go on a camping trip with Snoopy and some of his friends.

"That's a great idea!" Snoopy says. "After all, I *am* a Beagle Scout!"

Woodstock quickly gathers his friends.

"Follow me, troops," Snoopy says. "And I don't want to see anyone hanging around my feet!"

The birds are very nervous about the hike. They want to stay as close to Snoopy as possible, so they all fly onto the top of his Beagle Scout hat. *Well, at least they paid attention to some of what I said,* Snoopy thinks.

It isn't long before the birds get very homesick, so Snoopy decides to cut the trip short. "It's the perfect time to head home," Snoopy tells them. They knock on Charlie Brown's door. "We're just in time for dinner."

"Well, I guess now you probably just want to relax for a while," Charlie Brown says.

Snoopy looks at him in shock. Relax? Is he kidding? Snoopy pulls out a guitar. It's time for a little after-dinner music!

"I guess you'll never be an ordinary dog, will you, Snoopy?" Charlie Brown says. "But you know what? I don't think I'd have it any other way."

Neither would I! Snoopy thinks happily. *Neither would I!*

PEANUTS
Go Fly a Kite, CHARLIE BROWN!

By Charles M. Schulz
Adapted by Cordelia Evans
Illustrated by Will Yak

SIMON SPOTLIGHT
New York   London   Toronto   Sydney   New Delhi

Today the sky is blue, the sun is shining, and there's a strong breeze. It's the perfect kind of day for Charlie Brown's *favorite* activity.

"Bye, Sally," he tells his sister. "I'm going to go fly a kite!"

Then he grabs his new blue kite and heads outside.

Charlie Brown arrives at an empty field—empty except for one innocent-looking tree.

"You're a kite-eating tree, aren't you?" he asks the tree, but it doesn't respond. Charlie Brown is suspicious, but he's not about to let a tree stop him from flying his kite!

He starts to run with his kite, and just as it is about to catch a gust of wind . . . he feels a sharp tug on the string.

Charlie Brown turns to see what his kite is snagged on, and finds it stuck in the tree's branches.

"Aaugh!" Charlie Brown groans. "I *knew* this was a kite-eating tree!" he shouts. Then he stomps over to the tree to give it a piece of his mind.

"Now, look, tree. That's my kite you've got up there, and I want it back!" he says, shaking his fist. "You can't go grabbing every kite that flies by, you know! Now, give it back. Do you hear me?"

The tree says nothing.
"You can't argue with a kite-eating tree," Charlie Brown says to himself as he begins the sad walk home without his kite.

Charlie Brown gets to work making another kite—a red one this time.
"Back so soon?" Sally asks him.
"I'm hoping the kite-eating tree isn't in the mood for strawberry flavor,"
Charlie Brown replies as he heads outside with his new kite.
"Everyone likes strawberry flavor," Sally says. "Don't they?"

And sure enough, as soon as Charlie Brown starts running with the red kite . . . he feels that familiar tug on the end of the string. The tree has eaten his kite—again!

Now Charlie Brown is really angry. "If you don't let go of that kite," he yells at the tree, "I'll kick you right in the stomach!"

The tree says nothing. So Charlie Brown marches over and kicks its trunk as hard as he possibly can. But the tree still doesn't give up the kite. And now Charlie Brown's foot hurts.

"These kite-eating trees have hard stomachs," he says.

Charlie Brown goes home to make even more kites: yellow, green, and orange ones.

"Why are you making so many kites?" Sally asks.

"It liked the blueberry and the strawberry, and I bet it will like the lemon flavor too," Charlie Brown replies. "But I'd really like to find a flavor it *doesn't* like."

Sally thinks for a moment, then shrugs. "Try the lime green one!"

So Charlie Brown, along with Snoopy, heads back to the field with the yellow and green kites. Snoopy flies the yellow kite while Charlie Brown flies the green kite . . . or tries to, anyway.

The tree quickly eats Charlie Brown's kite, as usual. But he is surprised to see Snoopy flying the yellow kite high up, up, up in the air.

What did you expect? thinks Snoopy. *I'm the World's Greatest Kite Flyer!*

"I guess the tree doesn't like lemon flavor after all," Charlie Brown says. "I need to take note of that."

But when Charlie Brown attempts to fly the yellow kite himself, the tree eats it. The kite-eating tree seems to eat *any* kite Charlie Brown is flying.

"I can't stand it. I just can't stand it!" Charlie Brown exclaims.

Charlie Brown is determined not to feed the kite-eating tree any more kites! He marches up to the tree again and leans in close.

"What would you do if I decided not to fly any more kites this year?" he asks. When he doesn't get a reply, he shouts, "You'd starve to death, that's what you'd do!"

Charlie Brown is still mad, but a small part of him feels better knowing that the tree needs him. *It's nice to be needed*, Charlie Brown thinks to himself.

That's when he runs into Lucy and Linus.

"You hate that tree, don't you, Charlie Brown?" asks Linus.

Charlie Brown nods. "You know why I hate it? Because it's greedy, that's why! Even while it has a kite in its branches, it'll reach out and grab another one! It's like a little kid eating french fries. One is never enough!"

Linus and Lucy decide to check out the kite-eating tree for themselves. "Don't get too close," warns Charlie Brown as they walk away.

When she sees the tree, Lucy gets an idea. *If the kite-eating tree eats kites, maybe it also eats dirty blue baby blankets that certain little brothers need to stop carrying everywhere,* she thinks.

"I don't want to live in a world where kite-eating trees exist," says Linus sadly, as he looks up at the pieces of kite poking out of the tree.

That's when Lucy takes his blanket . . .

. . . and feeds it to the kite-eating tree, which gobbles it right up.

Linus stands in shock for a moment. "My own sister threw my blanket up in a kite-eating tree!" he wails, and runs to Charlie Brown and Snoopy to ask for help.

Snoopy immediately puts on his Rescue Squad hat.

"Here comes the captain of the Rescue Squad!" shouts Charlie Brown. "He's going to save Linus's blanket!"

"That silly beagle won't be able to save anything," says Lucy as Snoopy starts to climb the trunk of the tree. "Beagles can't climb trees!"

We can't? thinks Snoopy.

He continues to try to climb the tree anyway. He makes it about halfway up before he realizes Lucy is right.

Why am I doing this? he thinks as he slides to the ground with a loud *thud!*

"Now I'll never get my blanket back!" cries Linus. "Just like Charlie Brown has never gotten a kite back!"

The tree shudders and Linus's blanket falls out, along with several old, chewed-up kites.

"I thought I'd never see my blanket again," says Linus, hugging it close.

"Look, Charlie Brown, there's one good kite left!" Linus exclaims, pointing to a perfectly shaped kite in the pile of mangled ones.

"You're right!" says Charlie Brown. "But . . . there's no more wind to fly it in."

Snoopy has an idea . . . and calls on Woodstock and the Beagle Scouts to help him with it.

"Look, Snoopy!" says Charlie Brown. "For once I got the better of the kite-eating tree. I'm finally flying a kite!"

Snoopy raises his eyebrows.

"Sort of," Charlie Brown adds, when he realizes *how* he is flying a kite. "Good grief!"

PEANUTS®
Kick the Football,
CHARLIE BROWN!

By Charles M. Schulz

Adapted by Cordelia Evans

Illustrated by Scott Jeralds

SIMON SPOTLIGHT

New York   London   Toronto   Sydney   New Delhi

Every year when football season starts, Charlie Brown attempts to achieve one of his many goals in life: to kick a football and watch it soar through the air. And every year when Charlie Brown tries to do this, the same thing happens. It all starts with his friend Lucy.

"Over here, Charlie Brown!" says Lucy. "I've got a brand-new ball. I'll hold it, and you come running up and kick it."

"A brand-new ball!" Charlie Brown shouts. "Wow, this is a real treat."

Charlie Brown gets a running start and approaches Lucy. But just as he goes to kick the ball, Lucy pulls it away. Charlie Brown goes flying into the air and lands with an "AAUGH!" on his back.

"Why did you take the ball away?" Charlie Brown asks Lucy angrily.

"It suddenly occurred to me that if I let you kick it, it wouldn't be new anymore," Lucy explains.

The next time it's the same story.

"Charlie Brownnnnn!" calls Lucy in a singsong voice. "Come on. I'll hold the football, and you come running up and kick it," Lucy says. "I have a surprise for you this year."

A surprise? thinks Charlie Brown. *That must mean she isn't going to pull the football away. She's going to be surprised when she sees how far I kick that ball!*

Just like last year, Charlie Brown runs quickly at the football that Lucy's holding. Just like last year, the second he goes to kick it, Lucy pulls it away. And just like last year, Charlie Brown goes flying into the air and lands with an "AAUGH!"

"And now for the surprise," Lucy says to Charlie Brown, who can't bring himself to get up quite yet. "Would you like to see how that looked on instant replay?"

The next time Charlie Brown sees Lucy holding a football, he won't even give her a chance to talk. "No!" he shouts. "You must think I'm crazy—you say you'll hold the ball, but you won't! You'll pull it away, and I'll fall again."

"Why, Charlie Brown, I wouldn't think of such a thing," insists Lucy, smiling calmly. "I'm a changed person. Isn't this a face you can trust?"

"All right," Charlie Brown agrees begrudgingly. "You hold the ball, and I'll come running up and kick it."

This time Charlie Brown is only a little surprised when Lucy pulls away the football and he lands on his back.

"I admire you," Lucy tells him. "You have such faith in human nature."

So Charlie Brown avoids Lucy. But she knows just where to find him.

"What's up?" Sally asks when she opens the door to her house to see Lucy standing there.

"Tell your brother to come out," says Lucy. "I'll hold the ball, and he can come running up and kick it."

"She's here again," Sally says to Charlie Brown inside. "Why does she think she can fool you over and over?"

"You don't really believe my brother will fall for this, do you?" Sally asks Lucy. "I mean, after all, how often do you think you can fool someone with the same trick?"

But Charlie Brown is already following Lucy outside.

Sally stands on the front stoop and watches as Charlie Brown runs to kick the football, Lucy pulls it away, and Charlie Brown goes flying and lands on his back with an "AAUGH!"

"Pretty often, I guess," Sally remarks as Charlie Brown goes back into the house, his head spinning.

But Charlie Brown is not a quitter—and he is *not* going to give up!
"I'm going to kick that football all the way to the North Pole!" he declares.

His friends are very supportive. They believe in Charlie Brown, too! And besides, they all know how much Lucy loves her tricks . . . and they would love to see Charlie Brown get the better of her.

Linus offers to lend Charlie Brown his blanket as a good-luck charm.

Sally gives Charlie Brown a big, encouraging hug.

"Isn't this part of football, anyway?" she asks, squeezing him tight. "We're practicing right now, big brother!"

"That's tackling, not hugging," says Charlie Brown, gasping for air.

For help training, Charlie Brown turns to
his most trusted friend and adviser: Snoopy.

Snoopy puts him to work, making him run laps to strengthen his legs
and practice drills over and over again. He's a great coach!

After all, Snoopy's had a lot of experience with his own team.

Charlie Brown even has a dream that night that he kicks the football. And not only does he kick it, but it soars higher into the air than any football in the world! Charlie Brown knows he can do this.

The next day Charlie Brown is ready to face Lucy. And she's ready for him. She sets herself up on the grass.

"So, I'll hold the ball, Charlie Brown, and you come running—" she begins.

"Lucy!" Rerun interrupts. "Mom says to come in for lunch."

Lucy ignores her little brother and turns back to Charlie Brown. "You come running up and kick it—"
"She says right now!" shouts Rerun.
"Oh, good grief!" says Lucy.

"That's all right. We'll do it some other time," says Charlie Brown. He's getting a little nervous anyway.

"No, Rerun can take my place," says Lucy, handing him the football. She goes inside.

"Me?" says Rerun. He kneels on the grass and holds the football steady. *This time I'll do it!* thinks Charlie Brown. *Rerun would never pull the ball away!*

"Here we go!" he shouts, gearing up to run at the ball.

A few minutes later Rerun carries the football inside to where Lucy is eating her lunch.

"What happened?" she asks. "Did you pull the ball away? Did he kick it?"

Rerun smiles mysteriously. "You'll never know."

PEANUTS®
Lose the Blanket, LINUS!

By Charles M. Schulz
Adapted by Tina Gallo
Illustrated by Robert Pope

SIMON SPOTLIGHT
New York   London   Toronto   Sydney   New Delhi

This is Linus. Linus loves his blanket more than anything in the world.

His blanket is soft. It makes him feel happy. He likes the way the fabric feels against his cheek. It makes him feel calm. When Linus holds his blanket, he feels like everything will be all right, no matter what happens.

His sister, Lucy, however, thinks differently. His blanket annoys her. "When are you going to get rid of that silly blanket?" she asks.

"It's not silly," Linus replies. "It makes me feel happy. Maybe if you had a blanket, you wouldn't be so crabby."

"Crabby? Who's crabby?" Lucy shouts.

I guess from now on I'll keep my suggestions to myself, Linus thinks.

"THIS IS IT!" Lucy shouts. Her voice startles Linus, and he jumps. Lucy grabs his blanket and runs off.

I wonder what that was all about, Linus thinks. He shrugs and turns to pick up his blanket. But his blanket is nowhere to be found!

Linus is still frantically searching for his blanket when Lucy returns. She has a huge grin on her face.
"I buried your blanket!" she tells him.

Linus can't believe his ears.

"You *buried* my blanket?" he yells. "You can't do that! I'll die without that blanket! I'll be like a fish out of water! I'll die! I'll die!"

Lucy just stares at Linus. She doesn't say a word.

Linus gets very angry. "Tell me where you buried it!" he demands.

Linus tells his friend Charlie Brown what happened.
"She what?" Charlie Brown asks.

"She buried my blanket, Charlie Brown!" Linus cries.
"She said she was going to cure me of the habit once
and for all, so she buried my blanket!"

Linus looks around at his huge backyard. "How am I
ever going to find it?" he says.

Charlie Brown decides to sleep over at Linus's house to help him get through the first night without his blanket. He pulls up a chair and watches Linus as he sleeps.

"Ohhhh . . . ," Linus moans. He tosses and turns in his sleep.

This is going to be a long night, Charlie Brown thinks.

Suddenly Linus opens his eyes. He looks at Charlie Brown hopefully. "Is it morning yet?" he asks.

"No, it's only ten o'clock," Charlie Brown replies.

"Ten o'clock?!" Linus exclaims. This night is going to last forever!" He lets out a long sigh. "Anyway, Charlie Brown, it's nice of you to sit up with me this first night."

Charlie Brown smiles at Linus. "This is what friends are for," he says.

"Good old Charlie Brown!" Linus says.

A little while later, Linus closes his eyes again. *Ah, that's good,* Charlie Brown thinks. *He's finally gone to sleep. Maybe if he makes it through the night without his blanket, he'll be all right. Sleep is just what he needs.*

"WELL, HOW'S HE DOING?" Lucy's voice booms through the bedroom as she stomps in to check on Linus.

"So much for a good night's rest," Charlie Brown says with a sigh.

The next day Lucy comes over to chat with Charlie Brown.

"You think I'm being mean because I buried Linus's blanket, don't you?" she asks.

Charlie Brown doesn't say anything.

"Well, I'm not!" Lucy continues. "I'm really doing him a favor! He's too weak to ever break the habit by himself. He's as weak as . . . why, he's as weak as *you* are, Charlie Brown!"

I don't think I like that comparison, Charlie Brown thinks.

Charlie Brown tries everything he can think of to help his friend. "I have a suggestion, Linus," he says. "Why don't you let me try to give you a substitute? Would you like this dish towel?"

Linus does not like that idea at all. "Would you give a starving dog a rubber bone?" he asks. "No thank you!"

Charlie Brown shrugs. "I'm out of ideas," he says.

From the moment Linus wakes up the next day, he feels terrible. He goes into the kitchen and takes out a box of cereal for breakfast. He pours some milk on the flakes and takes a bite. He pushes the bowl away. *I can't even eat . . . everything tastes sour,* he thinks.

Lucy, meanwhile, feels just fine. She is relaxing, reading a book. "Please tell me where you buried it," Linus begs.

Lucy doesn't answer.

"I've just got to find that blanket, Charlie Brown," Linus says. "Lucy won't tell me where she buried it, so I've got to dig until I find it." Linus shovels as he speaks.

Charlie Brown admires Linus's determination. "Good luck!" he calls after him.

Linus keeps digging. "Got to find it! Got to find it!" he says to himself. "Got to dig everywhere until I find that blanket! Got to find it! Got to find it!" Linus says.

"Got to find it!" Linus repeats as he continues on his way.

Snoopy can't understand why Linus is so upset. Finding things that are buried is easy for Snoopy! He sniffs around a little bit . . . and there it is!

"MY BLANKET!" Linus yells. "Oh, Snoopy! You found it! You found it! You found it!" Linus says over and over again.

When Linus finally lets him go, Snoopy promptly goes back to his doghouse. *I've done my good deed for the day,* he thinks. *Time for a nap!*

The next day Charlie Brown talks to Lucy about Linus and his blanket. "I hear Linus got his blanket back," Charlie Brown says.

Lucy frowns. "Yeah, your nosy dog found it and dug it up," she says. "Oh well. I don't care anymore. I'm through trying to help people. They never appreciate it, anyway."

"NOSY DOG!" she shouts.

"Hee hee!" Snoopy giggles. He isn't the least bit sorry he helped Linus get his blanket back!

Linus can't stop hugging his blanket. "My blanket! I got it back! I can't believe it! My good old blanket!" Linus says.

He holds it out in front of him and studies it. "It's been buried beneath the ground for days and days," he says. "It's dirty, it's ragged, it's torn, and it's even a little moldy."

Then he hugs it again. "But it's *my* blanket!" he says with a happy sigh.

"You do realize you can't hold on to your blanket forever," Lucy says. "Someday you are going to have to lose the blanket, Linus, whether you like it or not."

Linus tries to imagine being a grown-up. He pictures going to work in a suit and a tie. He knows he probably can't bring his blanket to work with him.

Linus nods. "That's very true, Lucy," he says. "I realize *someday* I'll have to give up my blanket."

He grins at Lucy. "But not today!"
Lucy rolls her eyes. "I give up!" she says.

PEANUTS

Snoopy and Woodstock's Great Adventure

By Charles M. Schulz

Adapted by Lauren Forte

Illustrated by Scott Jeralds

SIMON SPOTLIGHT

New York   London   Toronto   Sydney   New Delhi

This is Snoopy. And these are his friends Conrad, Olivier, Bill, Harriet, and Woodstock.

It is such a beautiful day that Snoopy, the world-famous Beagle Scout, is leading his troops out into the wilderness.

"Charlie Brown, I just saw your dog go by. Where is he going?" Lucy asks.

"He's taking his friends to Point Lobos on a photo hike," he answers.

"Point Lobos?" Lucy responds. "Doesn't he know how far that is? How's he ever going to find it?"

Charlie Brown is not worried. Snoopy goes on adventures all the time.

"All right, troops," Snoopy calls out. "Let's have an equipment check. Bill, what did you bring?"

Bill chirps excitedly.

"A compass?" Snoopy says, surprised. "You think we're going to get lost? Woodstock, what did you bring?"

Woodstock holds up some rain gear.

"Rain gear? Good grief. It isn't going to rain."

Snoopy rolls his eyes as he looks at the rest of the things they brought. He tosses aside a flashlight from Olivier and a first-aid kit from Conrad. His friends are such worriers!

"All right, Harriet, how about you?" Snoopy barks.

Harriet smiles and proudly holds up a plate.

"An angel food cake with seven-minute frosting?" Snoopy says, relieved. "Well, I'm glad we have at least one sensible hiker in our group!"

Before they set out, Snoopy makes sure all the scouts have their cameras.

"Good," he says. Snoopy gestures to the forest ahead of them. "Now on today's photo hike, you'll get to take some beautiful, and maybe unusual, pictures . . ."

But when Snoopy turns around, the scouts are just taking photos with each other! "Not of yourselves!" says Snoopy. He turns and leads the group onto the path with a sigh.

The hike begins! As they walk, they stop along the way to take pictures of fluffy clouds, tall trees, and oddly shaped rocks.

But as they reach some very overgrown weeds, Snoopy calls out a warning, "All right, troops. We're entering tall grass. This could mean queen snakes! We should walk single file—"

"Or . . . vertical file," Snoopy says under his breath, as the birds all perch on top of his hat.

Snoopy walks through the field warily, on the lookout for queen snakes!

Once they've cleared the tall grass, Snoopy lets the birds back down onto the path. Luckily they didn't run into any snakes, but now the ground is bumpy, and the scouts are getting tired. Hiking is hard work.

Olivier chirps a question.

"A walking stick?" asks Snoopy. "You're right. We all should have walking sticks."

Olivier volunteers to gather walking sticks for everyone.

But when Olivier returns with the sticks, there's just one problem: They're all bird-size!

This is not so helpful, thinks Snoopy as they continue along the trail.

"Can someone get up in a tree or something and try to see where we're going?" Snoopy asks a few hours later. They have to be close to Point Lobos by now!

Bill silently wonders if his compass would have been helpful after all. It's easy to get lost in the woods.

"Harriet?" Snoopy calls on her. "Get up as high as you can and tell us what you see."

Harriet flies up onto the brim of Snoopy's hat to get a good look around.

"Actually, Harriet, I was hoping you'd get up a little higher than that," Snoopy says sarcastically.

Still, Harriet sees the way! She chirps that they are on the right path—in fact, they're almost there!

As the friends head up the final hill, Snoopy has an idea.

"When we get to the top," Snoopy says while panting, "we'll eat the angel food cake that Harriet brought."

Bill and Olivier chirp in agreement—they've really worked up an appetite!

But then Conrad chirps back angrily.

"What?" Snoopy cries. "Why can't we eat the cake at the top of the hill?"

Conrad chirps again.
"Because Harriet ate it at the bottom of the hill!" repeats
Snoopy. "Argh!"

But Snoopy can't stay mad at Harriet for long. As they round the top of the hill, they finally arrive at Point Lobos, and the view is spectacular.

Snoopy takes a deep breath and looks out over the water. "There it is, gang—the Pacific Ocean!"

The scouts stare at the scenery for a long time, thinking about how beautiful it looks, until Snoopy encourages them to get out their cameras.

"Now I want you to take a lot of pictures of what you see. That's what we're here for," Snoopy instructs as the birds start snapping away.

The scouts notice that there are colorful flowers growing all around the cliffs.

Snoopy points out a pretty purple one. Bill tries to take a picture of it, but there's a bee near the flower. It's buzzing and flitting all around, and Bill can't get a good shot!

"Be polite," Snoopy tells Bill. "Ask the bee if he minds moving."

This time it's Bill who rolls his eyes.

As the sun sets and it begins to get dark, the world-famous Beagle Scout and his troops set up camp for the night.

Of course no campout is complete without marshmallows. Conrad gets a tree branch and begins roasting them . . . all at once!

As the scouts get ready to settle in for the night, they munch on the huge pile of marshmallows and gaze at the starry sky.

"Look, there's a full moon tonight," Snoopy points out.

The birds are suddenly nervous and start chirping to Snoopy all at once.

"No. There aren't such things as werewolves. That's just a myth," Snoopy reassures them and continues. "But you know who really comes out when the moon is full?"

"The Werebeagle!" Snoopy shouts, making a scary face. All the birds dive into their sleeping bags for cover! Snoopy laughs and laughs.

"Okay, troops. It's bedtime," Snoopy says after everyone calms down. One by one the scouts hop onto Snoopy's sleeping bag and settle in for the night.

What a great day it was to hike with friends. Good night, Beagle Scouts!

PEANUTS

Snoopy for President!

By Charles M. Schulz
Adapted by Maggie Testa
Illustrated by Scott Jeralds

SIMON SPOTLIGHT
New York   London   Toronto   Sydney   New Delhi

It's a beautiful, sunny afternoon, and Snoopy is doing what he loves best—daydreaming on top of his doghouse. But then he hears something down below. It's Woodstock and the other birds hopping by, holding signs for different candidates for class president.

I had forgotten that this was an election year, thinks Snoopy.

One person who hasn't forgotten is Lucy. She wants her
little brother Linus to become the next class president.
   "But I could never be class president," says Linus. "Think
of the work. Think of the responsibility."
   "Think of the power," Lucy adds.
   Linus smiles. Actually, that sounds pretty good. "I'll do it!"
he shouts.

At school the next day Linus doesn't waste any time getting the word out.

"If I am elected class president, I will demand immediate improvements," he announces. "Any little dog who happens to wander onto the playground will *not* be chased away, but will be welcomed with open arms!"

Snoopy likes the sound of that!

But Linus has some competition. Pigpen is also running for class president, and some students are planning to vote for him. Lucy takes it upon herself to convince everyone in the school to vote for Linus.

"Hey, you!" she shouts on the playground. "Who are you gonna vote for?"

"Uh, Linus, for sure," the kid replies.
"Well, you better!" says Lucy. She
turns to Linus. "According to my
private poll, you now have eighty-five
percent of the vote."

The next day Violet approaches Linus. She's a reporter for the school paper. "Would you care to tell us what you intend to do if you're elected class president?" she asks.

"I intend to straighten things out!" Linus says passionately. "We are in the midst of a moral decline! We are—"

Violet interrupts him. "I'll just put down that you're very honored and will do your best if elected."

"The press is against me," whines Linus as Violet walks away.

But Linus isn't done with the press. Schroeder wants to take photographs of him and Pigpen for the school paper.

"Let's pose you both with a dog," explains Schroeder. Snoopy comes bounding out and steals the spotlight.

"Looking good, Snoopy," says Schroeder. "Maybe *you* should run for class president."

Snoopy likes the sound of that!

That afternoon Snoopy transforms his doghouse into campaign headquarters. Woodstock will be his campaign manager. He's got a lot of ideas about what Snoopy should do, but he gets so excited by them that he paces right off the doghouse!

My campaign manager isn't too bright, thinks Snoopy.

KLUNK!

CAMPAIGN HEADQUARTERS

Snoopy will just have to campaign by himself. He goes to school the next day and holds up a big sign with a paw print on it.

Lucy is not pleased. "I wouldn't vote for you if you were the last beagle on earth!" she tells him.

Snoopy starts to cry.

"All right," Lucy gives in. "If you were the last beagle on earth, I'd vote for you."
When Lucy walks away, Snoopy smiles.

Sally approaches Snoopy next. "I'm not sure if I'll vote for you or not," she says.

Once again Snoopy starts to cry.

"All right! All right!" Sally says. "I'll vote for you. Just stop crying!"

He's got a winning campaign strategy!

When Violet comes by, she asks Snoopy why she should vote for him.

"I mean, can you give me a reason?" she asks.

When Snoopy doesn't answer, she just walks away.

But Snoopy does know the answer. *For one thing, I'm kind of groovy!* he thinks.

Not much later Lucy comes by again.

"I think you're going about this all wrong," she tells Snoopy. "You've got to do more than just carry a sign. If you're going to get elected, you're going to have to shake a lot of hands and kiss babies."

Snoopy does *not* like the sound of that!

That evening Snoopy climbs back on top of his doghouse. Tomorrow is Election Day. Each candidate for class president will give one final speech before the students vote. What will Snoopy say in his speech?

I'll tell my latest anti-cat joke, he thinks. *The dog audience will love it. But wait . . . are there any dogs at the school aside from me?*

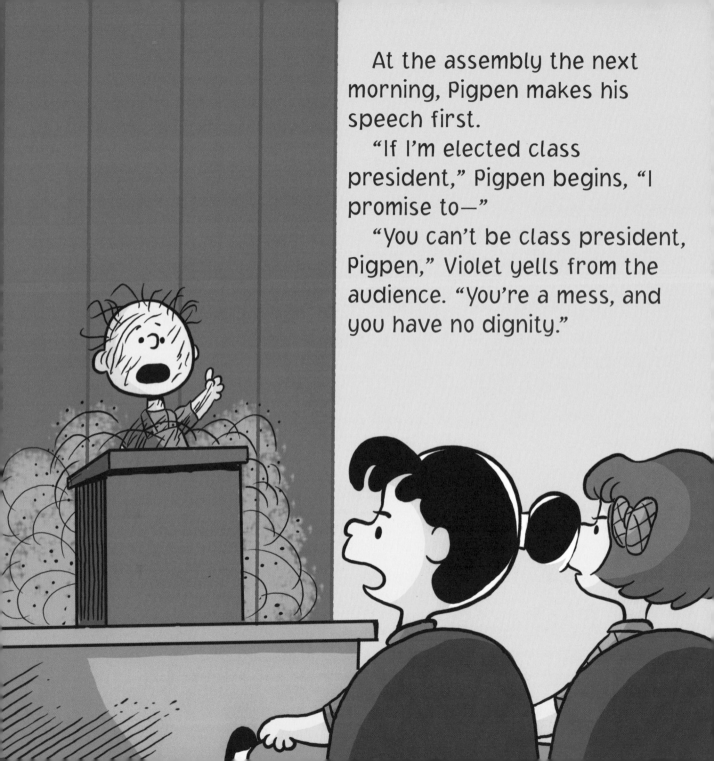

At the assembly the next morning, Pigpen makes his speech first.

"If I'm elected class president," Pigpen begins, "I promise to—"

"You can't be class president, Pigpen," Violet yells from the audience. "You're a mess, and you have no dignity."

But Pigpen isn't discouraged. He reaches down, picks up a top hat, and puts it on. He looks just like a dusty Abe Lincoln! Very presidential, Pigpen!

Linus goes up to the podium next. In the audience Lucy smiles. There's no way Linus can lose as long as he sticks to the script she wrote.

Linus clears his throat. "I want to talk to you this morning about the Great Pumpkin," he begins.

Everyone in the audience starts to laugh.

"AUGH!" Lucy screams.

The Great Pumpkin was the one thing Linus *wasn't* supposed to talk about. His chances of winning are over!

Snoopy is the final candidate to take the stage. Before he goes on, Schroeder asks Snoopy what he plans to say.

"Woof!" Snoopy replies.

"He's done for," Schroeder says to Linus.

But Snoopy is determined. He walks proudly to the podium, clears his throat, and lets out a confident bark. "Woof!"

The crowd goes wild.

A few hours later the votes are tallied. . . .

And Snoopy wins the election!

Linus and Pigpen are disappointed.

"I'm sorry you didn't get elected class president, Pigpen," says Linus.

"You too," says Pigpen. "Here we thought having photographs with a dog would get *us* votes, but instead, they all voted for the dog!"